This book belongs to:

...... Maryam & Zarah uddin ....

Class:

...... foundation 3 ....

Teacher:

.... usdadar Zainab ....

This book is about
Fiqh

'Rules on how to live an Islamic life.'

Words of Support

Dearest Moulana Shokat (May peace be with you),

Greetings! With great modesty I refer to your request about writing a prologue for Madrasah Islamiyah, Mount Pleasant's new syllabus الفنون الدراسية للادارة الملية الاسلامية . I am deeply sorry to inform you that I have been unable to fulfil your request; I am currently preoccupied with literary commitments, namely تذكرة اولى الاباب في تفسير الكتاب in these volatile and testing times.

I humbly beseech Allah Most High for everyone associated with Madina Masjid, Batley; for the completion of all planned projects; for their better health, strength, endurance and credence; and that, in this perishable life, He grants us the guidance to do such actions for the infinite life that will please our Master and His beloved Prophet ﷺ Aameen!

[Hadhrat Moulana] Yusuf Motala [Sahib DB]

[Darul Uloom, Holcombe, Bury]

9th Jumaa Dal Thani 1436

Foreword

It is an essential obligation to educate and nurture the youth of this Ummah. Whoever fervently participates in this will be worthy of reward. For the past few years, we have felt a profound need for an easy and child-friendly syllabus to educate our children in this country and especially at Madrasah Islamiyah. Beliefs, worship, transactions, social and moral etiquettes need to be communicated keeping in mind children's age and ability, so that they can read, comprehend and be able to practice, then hopefully their lives will insha Allah be in accordance with the Sunnah. This will protect them from ignorance and going astray.

All praise is for Allah Most High! Through the effort and sincere devotion of the management, staff and volunteers of Madrasah Islamiyah this aspiration has come to fruition. May Allah Most High accept this effort and sentiment as well as reward them in both of the worlds. May Allah the Almighty bless parents with the inspiration to take greater interest in their child's religious education and upbringing along with protecting everyone from calamities, misfortune and mishaps. Aameen.

Wassalaam

[Hadhrat Moulana] Sulaiman Bodiyat [Sahib DB]

[Imam and Ustaad at M.P.I.T.]

26 Jumaa Dal Ulaa 1436

17 March 2015

Introduction

الحمد لأهله والصلوة والسلام على أهلها

All praise is for Allah Most High who has granted us the light of knowledge for our guidance. Peace and salutations on our beloved Prophet Muhammad, the guiding light for mankind.

Allah Most High has created us as humans and has sent us into this world so that we may recognise and worship Him. For this recognition and worship Allah Most High sent His honourable prophets to guide humans with the light of knowledge. May Allah Most High grant our elders a high status in Jannah because, when they migrated to this country, one of their primary concerns was to establish Masaajid and Makaatib; hence these teachings are preserved and embedded within our future generations. The children of each generation are an amaanat and trust from Allah Most High placed in the hands of parents, community leaders, ulamaa and people in positions of authority and influence. Each individual will be accountable in the hereafter for his duties towards the preservation of these teachings.

Madrasah Islamiyah (Mount Pleasant Islamic Trust, Batley) is one of those institutions that has, for the past decades, facilitated and provided core Islamic learning and values for hundreds of children and instilled the light of prophetic guidance in their hearts.

We as a Madrasah constantly strive to attain the highest of standards in all aspects of Madrasah teaching through regular assessment and evaluation. We have felt the need for a bespoke syllabus to teach our children various subjects with a child-friendly approach using a level of English that is in accordance with their academic level. The demand for this interactive and friendly syllabus is even greater considering the times we live in and therefore can't be neglected, as we risk losing generations of children to the many distractions and tribulations of our time. With this imperative obligation in mind, after consultation, we at Madrasah Islamiyah have embarked on this journey to research, compile and publish a syllabus that will meet the requirements of this day and age in a child friendly way. It goes without saying that this will be a long journey and will demand a lot of effort, patience and commitment. We ask Allah Most High for His guidance, His help and above all to bless us with sincerity in fulfilling this mighty obligation. We also ask Him to accept this effort and to make this endeavour a means of benefiting our future generations. Aameen!

May Allah Most High reward everyone involved with this work, in any way or form, with the best of rewards in both worlds. Aameen! At this time we would like to mention, thank and make dua for the main team comprising Moulana Asjad Mamaniat, Moulana Abubakr Diwan and Brother Ahmed Hasan Patel (BSc, QTS, PGCE Secondary Physics), who have taken on this task and put a lot of time and effort into this. Furthermore, we would like to thank and make dua for all the ulama and professionals, who are constantly providing indispensable advice and consultation as well as helping with the proof-reading of publications.

We cannot forget to mention the dua and guidance received from our most senior elder Hadhrat Moulana Yusuf Motala Sahib (may his blessings endure), who has also honoured us by naming this series of publications. May Allah Most High grant him with a healthy and long life. Aameen!

M. Zakariya Akudi

Khadim Madrasah Islamiyah

5th Jumaa Dal Thani 1436

27th March 2015

How to Teach Using This Book

Learning Objectives (5 minutes)

Learning objectives are brief statements that describe what students will be expected to learn by the end of the lesson. These are differentiated to make learning appropriate to the child's ability.

Teachers will...

- Go through the learning objectives with students so they understand what they are expected to learn in the lesson.

- Make links to prior learning.

- Revisit at the end of the lesson to ensure students have met the objectives.

- Ensure that students tick the box to show they have met the objective.

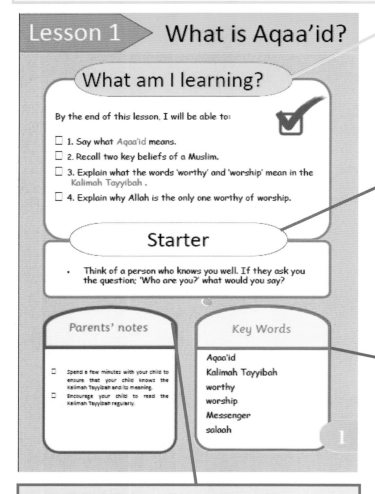

Lesson 1 — **What is Aqaa'id?**

What am I learning?

By the end of this lesson, I will be able to:

☐ 1. Say what Aqaa'id means.
☐ 2. Recall two key beliefs of a Muslim.
☐ 3. Explain what the words 'worthy' and 'worship' mean in the Kalimah Tayyibah.
☐ 4. Explain why Allah is the only one worthy of worship.

Starter

- Think of a person who knows you well. If they ask you the question: 'Who are you?' what would you say?

Parents' notes

☐ Spend a few minutes with your child to ensure that your child knows the Kalimah Tayyibah and its meaning.
☐ Encourage your child to read the Kalimah Tayyibah regularly.

Key Words

Aqaa'id
Kalimah Tayyibah
worthy
worship
Messenger
salaah

Starter (5 Minutes)

The purpose of the starter activity is to grab the students' attention at the very start of the lesson. This is covered before the topic introduction and before any teaching takes place.

It should be used to:

- Engage students in the new topic.

- Establish prior learning.

Keywords

These words are key in understanding the lesson correctly. Teachers should draw attention to these words by:

- Discussing them and their meanings.

- Displaying them on the board.

- Referring to them during the lesson.

Parents' Notes

This section is for parents to support their child's learning and upbringing.

Teachers should encourage students to:

- Read this at home with their parents.

- Carry out the activities suggested.

Who is Allah?

Allah is One, no one is like Him. He created us. We should worship no one except Allah Most High. He is the greatest and no one can challenge Him.

Allah is our Creator; He created everyone and everything. He is known as Al-Khaaliq, The Creator.

Allah is the All-Seeing, He sees everything. Allah is the All-Hearing, He hears everything. He is the most powerful and needs no help.

Allah Most High

10

Introduction

The introduction of the book is to help set the scene for the content covered in each lesson.

During this part of the lesson the teachers will...

- Go through the text with the students.

- Give students waiting time to allow them to reflect on what they have read.

- Ask students what they have understood from the text.

- Write the ideas on the board.

- Address any misconceptions.

- Highlight key points.

Lesson Content

This is the main part of the lesson which will help in achieving the learning objectives.

Teachers will...

- Make the lesson relevant and practical to the students by using examples, asking questions and relating stories.

- Keep students focussed on relevant tasks.

- Explain any difficult words

- Address any misconceptions.

Allah the All-Seeing

1 Allah Most High sees us but we cannot see Him.

2 Allah Most High sees everything that we do, even when we are alone.

3 Allah Most High sees all the good actions and bad actions we do.

4 For Allah Most High nothing is too far or too near. Everything is very clear.

5 Allah Most High sees everything, nothing is hidden from Him.

 'Al-Baseer' in Arabic means the All-Seeing. اَلْبَصِيرُ

13

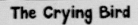

The Crying Bird

Our Prophet Muhammad ﷺ travelled to many different places with his companions, some were short journeys where they travelled by foot and some were long where they travelled on animals.

During one journey while they had stopped for a rest, our Prophet ﷺ left his companions to themselves for a short time. During his absence, one of the companions saw a mother bird called Hummara with its two young ones. The Sahaabi رضي الله عنه took the two young baby birds away from the mother bird. The mother bird was very troubled by this and started circling above in the air, beating its wings in pain and sorrow.

When the Prophet ﷺ came back and saw what was happening, he became very upset and asked: "Who has hurt the feelings of this bird by taking away its young? Return them to her at once!"

The Prophet's companion returned the baby chicks to the mother bird instantly.

(Muslim)

Moral of the story is.... Kindness is very important in Islam. Our Prophet ﷺ showed us in the above incident that we are not even allowed to hurt animals let alone other human beings. We have been taught to show kindness to humans whether they are Muslims or non-Muslims and also animals. If we see a person or an animal sad or upset then we should help to make them feel happy.

30

Stories are included in some chapters to further understanding.

At the end of the story teachers will...

• Focus on the moral of the story, reflecting learning objectives of that lesson and enab children to put their learning into context.

• Allow students to discuss what they have learnt.

• Ask them what they would change in their own li

Activity

A wide range of colour coded and differentiated activities have been formulated for students to consolidate their knowledge and understanding of each lesson. The activities are the most important part of learning as it allows the students and the teacher to see what has been learnt. Any mistakes made are another opportunity to learn. If a student has an incorrect answer ask them why it is incorrect and how would they change it to make it correct.

Activity

Fill in the missing words using the words below.

I live in an amazing world. Blue _____ that have no pillars holding it up. _____ that look like candy floss floating in the sky. Sea water, creating w_____ when I visit the beach. I see different boats in different sizes. I notice that some land is firm, easy for me to w_____ on. I also notice that some land is soft, easy for me to plant seeds in. _____ pours down and this helps the plants to g_____. All this, thanks to Allah Most High.

grow	sky	walk
waves	rain	clouds

Challenge

Write a poem about the beautiful world that Allah Most High has created for us using ideas from pages 11 and 12.

Colour-coded and Differentiated Activities

The activities are colour-coded according to the level of the task.

Teachers will...

- Provide students with support where needed

- Plan pair work

 These activities will assess students' recall and knowledge of facts, terms, basic concepts, information and answers.

 These activities will assess students' comprehension skills. They will demonstrate basic understanding of facts and ideas.

 These activities will assess students' ability to analyse and apply acquired knowledge and information.

 These activities will help students reflect and contemplate on their thoughts and actions.

 These activities will help students put into practice what they have learnt. The focus will be on practical aspects of learning. This is the most important part of the learning process.

 These activities will help students review learning which took place in previous books.

Guidelines for Parents

We aim to help our students progress with their learning and performance by creating a link with parents. Your support and encouragement as a parent plays a vital role in your child's development, therefore it is crucial to help and support your child with positive Islamic upbringing.

Learning Objectives

Each lesson begins with lesson objectives under the heading '*What am I learning?*' This allows students, teachers, parents and the institution to know from the very outset the learning objectives and outcomes of each lesson.

Parents' Notes

Each lesson includes brief information for parents to enable you to assist your child with their learning.

Activities

At the end of each lesson there are activities for students to complete to help them consolidate their learning and understanding.

Your Role

Your role as a parent is to ensure your child studies at home. Parents' notes are a useful guide to check if your child has met the learning objectives. It will also benefit your child greatly if you regularly check your child's book to see whether they have completed the activities.

6 A's in Understanding Your Child

Attention – Pay attention to your child and show interest in their learning.

Acceptance – Accept and recognise your child's shortcomings and mistakes.

Approval – Give your child approval when they do something good and positive.

Acknowledgement – Acknowledge and admit room for improvement for your child.

Appreciation – Appreciate and admire your child's qualities.

Affection – Show love and affection to your child.

CONTENTS PAGE

'Rules on how to live
an Islamic life.'

What am I learning?

By the end of this lesson, I will be able to...

- [ ] 1. Name the different types of rulings.
- [ ] 2. Describe the different types of rulings.
- [ ] 3. Sort the rulings into right and wrong actions.

Starter

- Before you come to Madrasah, what are the things that you always do?
- Before you come to Madrasah, what are the things that you sometimes do?

Parents' notes

- [ ] Ensure that your child is aware of the different types of rulings in Fiqh.
- [ ] Play games with your child, quiz them on different activities and its rulings. For example, is it fardh, waajib or sunnah to do miswaak during wudhu?
- [ ] Why not make a useful learning game like 'snap' or 'match the pairs'. One category should be the rulings, the other category should have the meaning and the third category should have different types of worship.

Key Words

Fardh

Waajib

Sunnah

Mustahab

Makrooh

Haraam

1

Rulings

There are rules for everything in this life. If there were no rules then people would do whatever they wanted and there would be disorder in this world.

For this reason our religion, Islam, is also based on rules which are set by Allah Most High. We understand the rules of Allah Most High from the Qur'aan Kareem and the teachings of Prophet Muhammad صَلَّى اللهُ عَلَيْهِ وَسَلَّم.

The rules have been divided into many types to help us practice our religion in the correct manner.

The Different Types of Rulings

Fardh
فَرْض

A compulsory act.
Example: Praying five daily salaah.

Waajib
وَاجِب

A compulsory act.
Example: Praying Eid salaah.

Sunnah
سُنَّة

An act which Prophet Muhammad ﷺ strongly encouraged.
Example: Doing miswaak.

Mustahab
مُسْتَحَب

An act which is liked and encouraged.
Example: To face the Qiblah whilst making wudhu.

Makrooh
مَكْرُوْه

An act which is disliked.
Example: Cleaning the nose with the right hand.

Haraam
حَرَام

An act which is forbidden in Islam.
Example: Disobeying parents.

Did you know?

The difference between fardh and waajib:
- If a person rejects a fardh act they will leave the fold of Islam.
- If a person rejects a waajib act they will not leave the fold of Islam but will be a sinner.

Activity

Match the ruling to the correct definition.

Fardh فرض	An act which is disliked.
Waajib واجب	An act which Prophet Muhammad ﷺ strongly encouraged.
Sunnah سنة	A compulsory act. If a person rejects it they will be a sinner.
Mustahab مستحب	A compulsory act. If a person rejects it they will leave the fold of Islam.
Makrooh مكروه	An act which is liked and encouraged.
Haraam حرام	An act which is forbidden in Islam.

Activity

In your own words write down the meanings.

Fardh فرض	
Waajib واجب	
Sunnah سنة	
Mustahab مستحب	
Makrooh مكروه	
Haraam حرام	

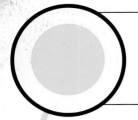

Activity

Fill in the gaps with the different types of rulings.

Fasting in the month of Ramadhan is compulsory,

so it is

<u>Fardh</u>

Lying is prohibited in Islam,

so it is

_____

Prophet Muhammad صَلَّى اللّٰهُ عَلَيْهِ وَسَلَّمَ strongly encouraged us to start all good things from the right hand side,

so it is

_____

Praying Fajr salaah is compulsory and if a person denies it they will leave the fold of Islam

so it is

_____

Prophet Muhammad صَلَّى اللّٰهُ عَلَيْهِ وَسَلَّمَ strongly encouraged sitting down on the floor whilst eating,

so it is

_____

To pray three rak'aats of Witr is a must. If a person rejects it they will not leave the fold of Islam, so it is

_____

Drinking alcohol is forbidden,

so it is

_____

Spitting in a public place is disliked,

so it is

_____

To clean the nose with the right hand is undesirable,

so it is

_____

Now go back to the 'What am I learning?' section for this lesson and tick if you have met the objectives.

What am I learning?

By the end of this lesson, I will be able to...

☐ 1. Say what najaasah (impurity) means.

☐ 2. List at least three types of najaasah (impurity).

☐ 3. Identify when my body or clothes become najis (impure).

☐ 4. Identify when it becomes fardh or sunnah to wash the najaasah (impurity).

☐ 5. Know the difference between the state of taahir (purity) and najis (impurity).

Starter

When you hear the word cleanliness, what comes to your mind?

Parents' notes

☐   Encourage your child to change their clothes regularly, especially their socks.

☐   Spend time with your child cleaning and washing, so that they understand the concept of cleanliness. If possible, give your child a list of things to clean by themselves.

☐   Explain to your child why we must stay clean.

Key Words

Najaasah

Najis

Taahir

Impurity

Impure

Pure

Review

How much do you remember?
Match the words to their meanings.

Tahaarah

Qiblah

Qur'aan Kareem

Miswaak

Istinjaa

Islam

Fiqh

Wudhu

- Religious book

- A special twig used to clean the teeth and the mouth.

- To stay clean.

- The direction of the Ka'bah.

- Rules on how to live an Islamic life.

- The way of life shown by our Prophet Muhammad صَلَّى اللهُ عَلَيْهِ وَسَلَّمَ.

- Cleaning your private parts with water and tissue after using the toilet.

- A special way of washing ourselves with water.

Review

Circle the correct words in the activity.

I needed to go to the toilet. I covered my head / arms and I rolled up my trousers / sleeves. I read the dua beginning with اَللّٰهُمَّ / غُفْرَانَكَ. I took off my socks and entered the toilet with slippers / barefoot. I entered with my left / right foot first.

I made sure the door was open / closed so no one could see me. I stood / sat down to use the toilet. I did not eat, drink or talk in the toilet room. I read my book / nothing in the toilet room. I cleaned my private parts with water and tissue / towel using my left / right hand. I made sure I rushed / took my time and made sure no stool / soap was on my body or clothes.

After using the toilet I made sure the toilet seat was wet / dry and clean / dirty. I did not flush / flushed the toilet. Thereafter I washed my hands using water and soap. I left the toilet with my left / right foot first and read the dua for leaving the toilet beginning with اَللّٰهُمَّ / غُفْرَانَكَ.

9

Tahaarah

Tahaarah means to stay clean and pure. This is very important in the life of a Muslim.

Najaasah means impurity. Things which make our body, clothes or surroundings impure are known as najaasah.

If our body, clothes or surroundings are pure, they are known as taahir.

If our body, clothes or surroundings are impure, they are known as najis.

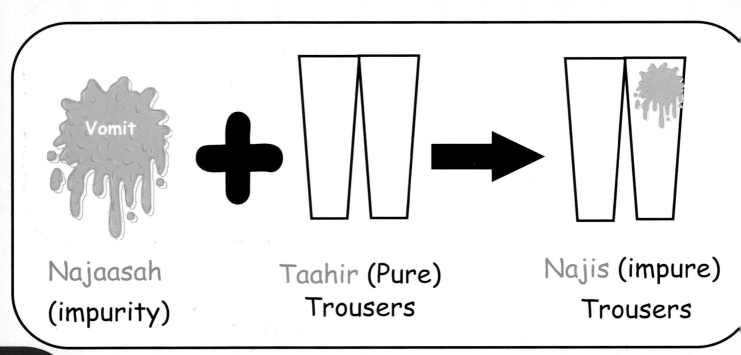

Najaasah (impurity)   Taahir (Pure) Trousers   Najis (impure) Trousers

Najaasah

1 The following things are najaasah (impurity):

- blood
- urine
- stool
- alcoholic drinks
- vomit

2 If the najaasah (impurity) is larger than the size of a 50p coin then it is fardh to wash it off our body or clothes.

Salaah will be invalid with the above najaasah (impurity).

3 If the najaasah (impurity) is smaller than the size of a 50p coin then it is sunnah to wash it off our body or clothes.

Salaah will be valid with the above najaasah (impurity) but it will be against the sunnah.

If najaasah comes into contact with the body or clothes immediately wash it off.

Activity

Tick the najaasah which makes our body or clothes najis.

mud	alcohol	water	ketchup
urine	juice	stool	sand
chocolate	blood	saliva	vomit

Activity

Label the diagram below correctly with the words najaasah, najis and taahir. In the table tick the correct boxes to show whether it is najaasah, najis or taahir.

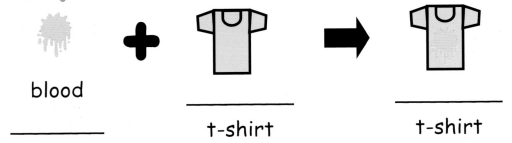

blood

_____

_____
t-shirt

_____
t-shirt

	Najaasah (impurity)	Taahir (pure)	Najis (impure)
urine			
trousers with chocolate on			
crayon			
socks stained with blood			
alcoholic drinks			
shirt with vomit on			
vomit			
scarf with yoghurt			

Activity

Using a 50p coin, work out if the following stains on the t-shirt would be fardh or sunnah to wash off.

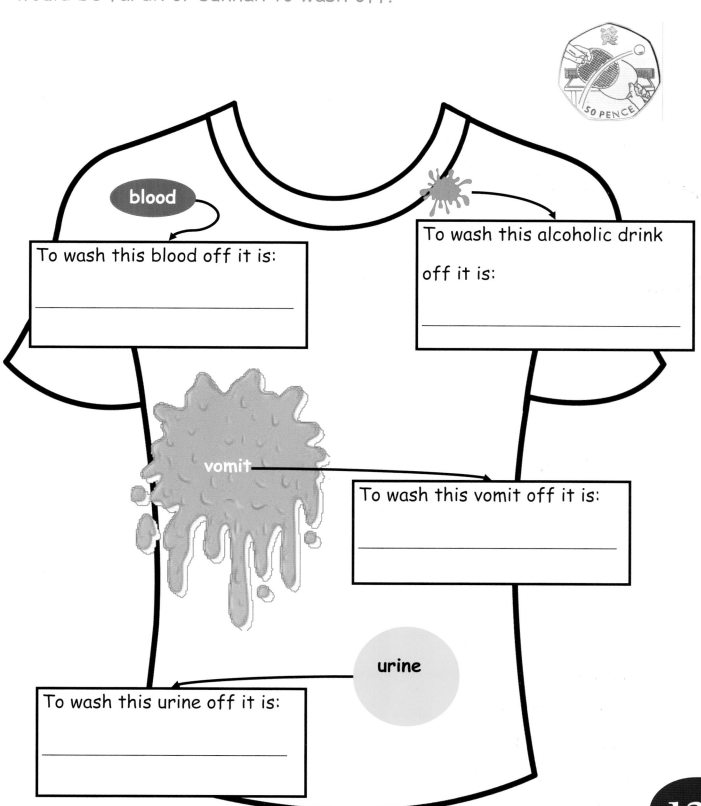

blood

To wash this blood off it is:
_____

To wash this alcoholic drink off it is:
_____

vomit

To wash this vomit off it is:
_____

urine

To wash this urine off it is:
_____

50 PENCE

13

Yusuf wants to pray Zuhr salaah but he has some stains on his body. Using a 50p coin, help him to work out which stains he has to wash off for his **salaah to be valid**.

blood		sauce	
Fardh to wash off		Fardh to wash off	
Sunnah to wash off		Sunnah to wash off	
No action needed		No action needed	
juice		**stool**	
Fardh to wash off		Fardh to wash off	
Sunnah to wash off		Sunnah to wash off	
No action needed		No action needed	
chocolate		**vomit**	
Fardh to wash off		Fardh to wash off	
Sunnah to wash off		Sunnah to wash off	
No action needed		No action needed	

14

Now go back to the 'What am I learning?' section for this lesson and tick if you have met the objectives.

What am I learning?

By the end of this lesson, I will be able to...

☐ 1. Demonstrate how to make sunnah wudhu in the correct order.

☐ 2. Label all the acts of wudhu with the correct ruling.

☐ 3. Explain the consequences of missing out a fardh act of wudhu.

Starter

Discuss:

• Would you meet a king with a dirty face or dirty hands?

• Explain why?

Parents' notes

☐ Encourage your child to make sunnah wudhu all the time without missing out any steps.

☐ Encourage your child to make fresh wudhu when it breaks.

☐ Encourage your child to make wudhu before coming to madrasah.

Key Words

Ablution

Masah

Khilaal

Niyyah

Duaa

Miswaak

Wudhu

Before we perform salaah or touch the Qur'aan Kareem it is important that we are in the state of wudhu. Wudhu is the Arabic word for ablution.

We wash and wipe those parts of our body which have been mentioned in the Qur'aan kareem and shown by our Prophet Muhammad صَلَّى اللهُ عَلَيْهِ وَسَلَّم.

Fardh of Wudhu

There are four fardh of wudhu all of which must be completed fully. Not even a hair space should be left dry otherwise wudhu will not be valid.

1 Wash the whole face from the hairline of the forehead to the bottom of the chin and from one earlobe to the other, once.

2 Wash both the arms from the fingers up to and including the elbows, once.

3 Make masah (wipe) of one quarter of the head.

4 Wash the feet including the ankles, once.

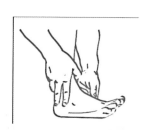

Did you know? Habit of making wudhu by only completing the fardh actions is makrooh. We will get less reward.

Sunnah Method of Wudhu

There are certain acts in wudhu which are sunnah. If sunnah acts are left out then wudhu will be completed but you will not get the full reward. There are thirteen steps altogether.

1 Make niyyah (intention).

I am doing wudhu

2 Read the duaa before wudhu.

بِسْمِ اللهِ وَالْحَمْدُ لِلّٰهِ ◯

'I begin in the name of Allah and praise be to Him.'

(Tabraani)

3 Wash both the hands including the wrists, three times, starting with the right.

4 Use a miswaak to clean the teeth and mouth with the right hand.

5 Gargle the mouth with water, three times, using the right hand.

6 Rinse the nose with water three times. Put water into the nose with the right hand and clean each nostril with the little finger of the left hand.

7 Wash the whole face from the hairline of the forehead to the bottom of the chin and from one earlobe to the other, three times.

8 Wash both the arms including the elbows, three times, starting with the right arm.

9 Make khilaal (pass wet fingers) of the fingers.

10 Make masah (wipe) of the whole head once.

11 Now using the same wet hands from step ten make masah (wipe) of your ears.

12 Wash the feet including the ankles, three times, starting with the right foot first. Make khilaal (pass wet fingers) of the toes.

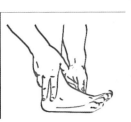

13 Read the duaa after wudhu.

اَللّٰهُمَّ اجْعَلْنِيْ مِنَ التَّوَّابِيْنَ ۝ وَاجْعَلْنِيْ مِنَ الْمُتَطَهِّرِيْنَ ۝

'Oh Allah make me from among those who repent for their sins and from among those who keep themselves pure.'
(Tirmidhi)

Whilst doing wudhu these acts are also sunnah:

a. Wash each part one after the other without pausing, so any one part does not dry up before the wudhu is completed.

b. To perform wudhu in the correct order.

c. To wash each part three times, except masah of the head and ears and khilaal of the fingers and toes.

Prophet Muhammad ﷺ said,

"He who makes wudhu and he does it perfectly, his sins fall off his body, even from under his finger nails.

(Bukhari & Muslim)

In order to save water whilst making wudhu, make sure the tap is not running in-between the washing of the different parts.

20

Any duaa or dhikr while in the bathroom should be made in the heart.

Activity

Once you feel you have mastered a step of wudhu fill in the table below with signatures from your partner, parent and teacher.

	Part of wudhu	1st My partner has seen me do it correctly	2nd My parent has seen me do it correctly	3rd My teacher has seen me do it correctly
1	niyyah			
2	duaa before wudhu			
3	hands			
4	miswaak			
5	gargle			
6	nose			
7	face			
8	arms			
9	khilaal			
10	masah of the head			
11	masah of the ears			
12	feet and khilaal			
13	duaa after wudhu			

Activity

Here you see the steps of sunnah wudhu. These are not in order. Your task is to put them in the correct order by numbering them from 1 to 13. Use pages 18, 19 and 20 to help you.

Wash the feet including the ankles, three times. Then make khilaal of the toes.	
Use a miswaak to clean the teeth and the mouth.	
Wash both the hands including the wrist, three times.	
Read the duaa before wudhu.	
Make masah of the whole head once.	
Gargle the mouth three times.	
Wash both the arms including the elbows, three times.	
Make khilaal of the fingers.	
Make niyyah (intention).	1
Clean the nose three times.	
Read the duaa after wudhu.	
Make masah of the ears.	
Wash the whole face, three times.	

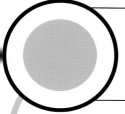

Activity

List the four fardh of wudhu.

1. _____

   _____

2. _____

   _____

3. _____

   _____

4. _____

   _____

If any one of the above fardh is left out, then what two things can we not do?

1. _____

2. _____

Abubakr goes swimming, his body becomes wet from head to toe. Is his wudhu complete? Explain your answer.

_____

_____

_____

_____

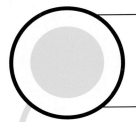

Activity

Zainab's Wudhu

Read the following actions (below) and decide if Zainab's wudhu is valid, invalid or valid but with less reward.

actions	valid with full reward	invalid	valid but with less reward
forgets to wash the face			
washes the arms before the face			
washes the face only once			
makes khilaal of the fingers and toes			
does masah of one quarter of the head			
forgets to do miswaak			
washes the feet three times including the ankles			
washes the arms leaving the elbows dry			

Now go back to the 'What am I learning?' section for this lesson and tick if you have met the objectives.

What am I learning?

By the end of this lesson, I will be able to...

- ☐ 1. Explain how to do ghusl in the sunnah way.
- ☐ 2. Understand the acts of ghusl with the correct ruling.
- ☐ 3. Explain why it is important to make ghusl regularly.

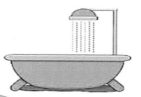

Starter

- In wudhu we wash certain parts of our body. Which parts of our body are important to wash in ghusl?

Parents' notes

- ☐ Encourage your child to perform ghusl regularly without wasting water.

- ☐ Encourage your child to have a sunnah ghusl, especially on Fridays.

- ☐ Encourage your child to be as independent as possible whilst making ghusl.

Key Words

Ghusl

Niyyah

Najaasah

25

Ghusl

Staying clean is an important part of a Muslim's life. In order to stay clean regularly we perform ghusl. Ghusl is a special way of washing our entire body with water. No part of our body must be left dry whilst making ghusl.

Cleanliness is loved by Allah Most High, it is half of our religion. Staying clean helps us to remain healthy.

Our Prophet Muhammad ﷺ has taught us how to perform ghusl correctly. This is known as the sunnah method of ghusl.

Fardh of Ghusl

Fardh of Ghusl

There are three fardh acts of ghusl all of which must be completed fully.

1 Gargle the mouth, once.

2 Put water in the nostrils.

3 Pour water over the entire body.

Make sure water reaches areas such as the inside of the belly button, behind the ears and under the arms.

Sunnah Method of Ghusl

The following sequence of making ghusl is sunnah. Doing ghusl in the sunnah way has greater reward.

1 Make niyyah (intention).

I am doing ghusl.

2 Recite Bismillah.

بِسْمِ اللَّه

3 Wash both hands including your wrists.

4 Wash the private parts.

5 Wash any najaasah or dirt that may be on the body.

6 Perform wudhu.

7   Pour water over the head three times.

8   Pour water all over the body three times in the following manner:

     a.   over the right side of the body starting from the shoulder.

     b.   over the left side of the body starting from the shoulder.

9   Rub the body and make sure not even a hair space is left dry.

10   Wash the feet.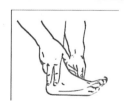

- Always do ghusl in a clean and private place.
- Use the toilet before doing ghusl. Do not urinate in the place where you are making ghusl.
- Use soap and shampoo to clean the body and hair properly.

Any dua or zikr while in the bathroom should be made in the heart.

Activity

Here you see the steps of sunnah ghusl. They are not in order. Put them in the correct order by numbering them from 1 to 10.

Number [ ] **WUDHU** To perform wudhu.	**Number** [1] **NIYYAH** To make intention for ghusl.	**Number** [ ] **FEET** To wash the feet.
Number [ ] **HEAD** To pour water over the head.	**Number** [ ] **RUB** To rub the body making sure no hair is left dry.	**Number** [ ] **BISMILLAH** To recite Bismillah.
Number [ ] **HANDS** To wash the hands up to the wrists.	**Number** [ ] **BODY** To pour water all over the body three times.	**Number** [ ] **NAJAASAH** To wash najaasah from any part of the body.
	Number [ ] **PRIVATE PARTS** To wash the private parts.	

Now go back to the 'What am I learning?' section for this lesson and tick if you have met the objectives.

What am I learning?

By the end of this lesson, I will be able to...

☐ 1. Explain what salaah is.

☐ 2. List the names of the five daily salaah.

☐ 3. Identify the times of each salaah.

☐ 4. List at least three virtues of salaah.

☐ 5. List at least two consequences of missing salaah.

Starter

1. How would you speak with someone who is in another country? What method would you use?
2. Now, what method do you think we should use to connect with our Creator?

Parents' notes

☐ Ensure your child knows the names of the five daily salaah.

☐ Help your child understand the different times of salaah.

☐ Remind your child of the virtues of performing salaah.

☐ Before salaah encourage your child to wear Islamic clothing which is clean and taahir.

Key Words

Virtue

Consequence

Fajr

Zuhr

Asr

Maghrib

Isha

31

Salaah

Salaah is the most important act of worship in Islam. Salaah is performed five times daily at fixed times.

Our Prophet Muhammad ﷺ has shown us how to pray salaah. It is a special type of worship gifted by Allah Most High to the Muslims. Praying salaah brings us closer to Allah Most High.

Names and times of salaah

| Fajr | Early morning prayer |

| Zuhr ظُهُر | Afternoon prayer |

| Asr عَصُر | Late afternoon prayer |

| Maghrib مَغْرِب | After sunset prayer |

| Isha عِشَاء | Night prayer |

Did you know? Allah Most High gave the five daily salaah as a gift to Prophet Muhammad صَلَّى اللهُ عَلَيْهِ وَسَلَّم when he went on the heavenly journey known as Me'raj.

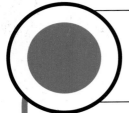

Activity

Match the salaah names to their correct description.

Asr   sunset prayer

Zuhr   night prayer

Isha   early morning prayer

Maghrib   afternoon prayer

Fajr   late afternoon prayer

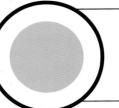

Activity

Write down three things that you know about salaah.

1. _____

_____

2. _____

_____

3. _____

_____

Virtues of Salaah

The Qur'aan explains that salaah stops a person from sins.

(Qur'an Surah Ankabut 29 Verse 45)

Praying the five daily salaah washes away sins.

(Bukhari, Muslim)

Salaah is the key to Jannah.

(Musnad Ahmad)

Consequences of Missing Salaah

When a person misses Asr salaah it is as though he has lost all his family and wealth.

(Bukhari)

A Muslim who misses a salaah without a valid reason will be committing a major sin.

(Al Haakim)

Did you know? Salaah will be the first thing a person will have to answer for on the Day of Qiyaamah.

Activity

Tell someone what you know about salaah.

I have told the following three people about the virtues of salaah:

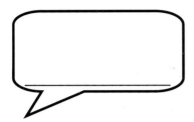  

I have told the following three people about the consequences of missing salaah:

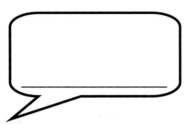  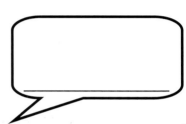

Activity

I pray my salaah because

_____

_____

I do not miss my salaah because

_____

_____

 Now go back to the 'What am I learning?' section for this lesson and tick if you have met the objectives.

What am I learning?

By the end of this lesson, I will be able to...

☐ 1. List all the conditions required before salaah.

☐ 2. Explain the conditions required before salaah.

☐ 3. Explain what happens to our salaah if any of these conditions are not met.

Starter

- Discuss with the person next to you the things that are important before performing salaah.

Parents' notes

☐ Encourage your child to listen to the adhaan before salaah.

☐ After adhaan make it a practice of performing salaah straight away.

☐ Give your child their own prayer mat and prayer cap or scarf.

☐ Ensure your child knows the direction of the Qiblah at home.

Key Words

Taahir

Qiblah

Niyyah

Condition

Before we touch the Qur'aan Kareem we need to have wudhu.

In a similar way before performing salaah, there are seven conditions that we need to meet for our salaah to be valid.

If any of the seven conditions are not met then our salaah will be invalid.

The **Qiblah** from England is towards the South East.

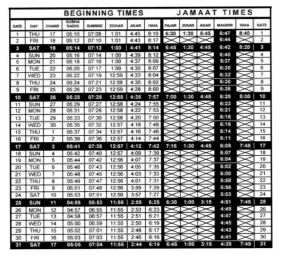

			BEGINNING TIMES					JAMAAT TIMES					
DATE	DAY	CHAND	SUBHA SADIQ	SUNRISE	ZOHAR	ASAR	ISHA	FAJAR	ZOHAR	ASAR	MAGRIB	ISHA	DATE
1	THU	17	05:10	07:08	1:01	4:45	8:19	6:30	1:30	5:45	6:47	8:40	1
2	FRI	18	05:12	07:10	1:01	4:43	8:17				6:44		2
3	SAT	19	05:14	07:12	1:00	4:41	8:14	6:45	1:30	4:45	6:42	8:20	3
4	SUN	20	05:16	07:14	1:00	4:39	8:12				6:40		4
5	MON	21	05:18	07:16	1:00	4:37	8:09				6:37		5
6	TUE	22	05:20	07:17	1:00	4:35	8:07				6:35		6
7	WED	23	05:22	07:19	12:59	4:33	8:04				6:32		7
8	THU	24	05:24	07:21	12:59	4:30	8:02				6:30		8
9	FRI	25	05:26	07:23	12:59	4:28	8:00				6:28		9
10	SAT	26	05:28	07:25	12:58	4:26	7:57	7:00	1:30	4:45	6:25	8:00	10
11	SUN	27	05:29	07:27	12:58	4:24	7:55				6:23		11
12	MON	28	05:31	07:28	12:58	4:22	7:53				6:21		12
13	TUE	29	05:33	07:30	12:58	4:20	7:50				6:18		13
14	WED	30	05:35	07:32	12:57	4:18	7:48				6:16		14
15	THU	1	05:37	07:34	12:57	4:16	7:46				6:14		15
16	FRI	2	05:39	07:36	12:57	4:14	7:44				6:11		16
17	SAT	3	05:41	07:38	12:57	4:12	7:42	7:15	1:30	4:45	6:09	7:45	17
18	SUN	4	05:42	07:40	12:57	4:09	7:39				6:07		18
19	MON	5	05:44	07:42	12:56	4:07	7:37				6:04		19
20	TUE	6	05:46	07:43	12:56	4:05	7:35				6:02		20
21	WED	7	05:48	07:45	12:56	4:03	7:33				6:00		21
22	THU	8	05:49	07:47	12:56	4:01	7:31				5:58		22
23	FRI	9	05:51	07:49	12:56	3:59	7:29				5:56		23
24	SAT	10	05:53	07:51	12:56	3:57	7:27				5:53		24
25	SUN	11	04:55	06:53	11:56	2:55	6:25	6:30	1:00	3:15	4:51	7:45	25
26	MON	12	04:57	06:55	11:55	2:53	6:23				4:49		26
27	TUE	13	04:58	06:57	11:55	2:51	6:21				4:47		27
28	WED	14	05:00	06:59	11:55	2:50	6:19				4:45		28
29	THU	15	05:02	07:01	11:55	2:48	6:17				4:43		29
30	FRI	16	05:03	07:03	11:55	2:46	6:16				4:41		30
31	SAT	17	05:05	07:04	11:55	2:44	6:14	6:45	1:00	3:15	4:39	7:45	31

We can find out the correct times to pray **salaah** using the local **salaah timetable**.

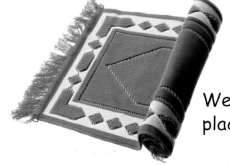

We perform our **salaah** on a **pure** place.

Seven Conditions Before Salaah

1 Our body must be taahir.
Make sure you have wudhu.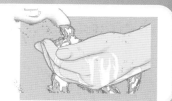

2 Our clothes must be taahir.

3 The place where we are performing salaah must be taahir.

4 Certain parts of our body must be covered.

5 The time of salaah must be correct.

6 We must face the Qiblah.

7 We must make niyyah.

I am praying 2 rak'aats fardh of Fajr salaah.

Activity

Circle the conditions that are important **before** salaah.

clothes must be white	wait for the imaam	place must be taahir	pray the Qur'aan
clothes must be taahir	wait for adhaan	face Madinah Munawwarah	body must be covered
face the Qiblah	drink water	apply perfume	make niyyah

Can you state the **two** conditions which are missing above?

1._____

2._____

Now go back to the 'What am I learning?' section
for this lesson and tick if you have met the objectives.

What am I learning?

By the end of this lesson, I will be able to...

- [ ] 1. Name the eight positions of salaah.
- [ ] 2. Describe the eight positions of salaah.
- [ ] 3. Demonstrate the eight positions of salaah.
- [ ] 4. Pray two rak'aats of salaah in the correct order.

Starter

- When are we nearest to Allah Most High?

Parents' notes

- [ ] Perform salaah with your child so that they become accustomed to reading salaah.
- [ ] Observe your child when they are reading salaah.
- [ ] Ask your child to observe your salaah.
- [ ] Make a salaah chart. Give your child incentives when they have read salaah.
- [ ] If your child misses salaah explain to them the consequences of not reading salaah and the rewards of performing it.
- [ ] Lead by example. Children watch us more than they listen to us. If you pick up a prayer mat as soon as the adhaan is called so will your child.

Key Words

Rak'ah

Rak'aat

Takbeer Tahreemah

Qiyaam

Ruku

Qawmah

Sajdah

Jalsah

Qa'dah Aakhirah

Salaam

Salaah

Before we start learning how to pray two rak'aats of salaah, it is important that we learn the main eight positions of salaah. This will make it easy for us to perform salaah correctly.

When we perform salaah it is very important that we concentrate all the time and remember that we are standing in front of Allah Most High.

The eight positions of salaah

Takbeer Tahreemah

The first Allahu Akbar

Qiyaam

Standing

Ruku

Bowing

Qawmah

Standing after ruku

Sajdah

Prostration

Jalsah

Sitting in-between both sajdahs

Qa'dah Aakhirah

Final sitting

Salaam

Final greeting to end the salaah

TOP TIP

When praying salaah do not fidget because this affects our concentration.

43

Boys' Salaah

How to learn to perform two rak'aats salaah using this book:

- Your teacher will show you how to perform each position of salaah correctly.

- Practice each position until it is perfect. After you have mastered all of the positions complete the activity on page 61.

- The recitation of Qur'aan and dua in salaah should be carried out softly. Whilst learning, recite loudly.

- All the Arabic duaas in salaah are on pages 58, 59 and 60.

1   Niyyah (Intention)

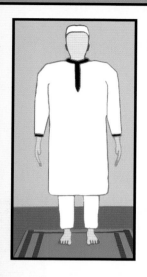

a. Stand upright facing the Qiblah, with the hands by the side and make the niyyah. For example:
"I am performing two rak'aats fardh of Fajr salaah."

b. Focus the eyes towards the place of sajdah (prostration).

2   Takbeer Tahreemah (The First Allahu Akbar)

a. Raise both hands up to the ear lobes with both palms facing the Qiblah.

b. Then whilst saying Allahu Akbar fold the hands as shown in step three.

3   Qiyaam (Standing) - Folding the hands

a. Place the left hand below the navel.

b. Place the right palm on the back of the left hand.

c. Make a circle with the right thumb and the right little finger gripping the left wrist.

d. Place the three middle fingers of the right hand on the left forearm, keeping them together.

45

4   Qiyaam (Standing) - Qir'aat (Recitation)

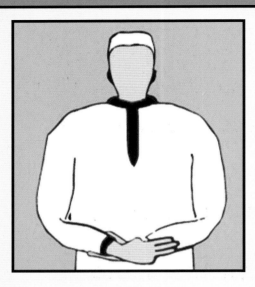

Now recite the following in order

a. Thanaa

b. Ta'awwudh

c. Tasmiyah

d. Surah Faatihah. Say Aameen softly at the end.

e. Tasmiyah

f. A surah (at least three verses)

5   Ruku (Bowing)

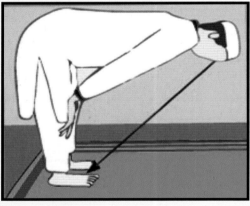

a. Whilst saying Allahu Akbar go into ruku.

b. In ruku hold both the knees wit the fingers spread out.

c. The arms should not touch the body.

d. Make sure the back is straight and i line with the head. The eyes should b looking at the feet.

e. Recite tasbeeh of ruku سُبْحَانَ رَبِّيَ الْعَظِيمِ least three times.

6 Qawmah (Standing after ruku)

a. Recite tasmee' سَمِعَ اللهُ لِمَنْ حَمِدَهُ whilst standing up from ruku, with the hands at the side.

b. Stand up straight and say the tahmeed رَبَّنَا وَلَكَ الْحَمْدُ.

c. Focus the eyes towards the place of sajdah (prostration).

d. Stay in this position until the whole body is relaxed.

7 First Sajdah (Prostration)

a. Now go into sajdah whilst saying Allahu Akbar.

b. Keep the back straight whilst going down.

c. Place the knees on the ground first, followed by the hands, then the nose and then the forehead.

d. The face should be placed between the hands with the fingers together, pointing towards the Qiblah.

e. The elbows should be off the ground.

f. Keep the toes on the ground pointing towards the Qiblah. At no point should they be raised.

g. Recite tasbeeh of sajdah سُبْحَانَ رَبِّيَ الْأَعْلَى at least three times.

h. Focus the eyes towards the nose.

8 Jalsah (Sitting in-between both sajdah)

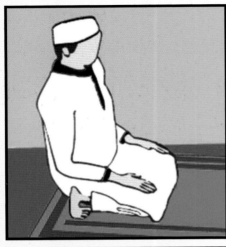

a. Sit up from sajdah, whilst saying Allahu Akbar.

b. Place both hands on the thighs, near the knees.

c. Sit on the left foot and have the right foot standing up with the toes pointing towards the Qiblah.

d. Stay in this position until the whole body is relaxed.

e. Focus the eyes towards the lap.

9 Second Sajdah (Prostration)

a. Whilst saying Allahu Akbar go into sajdah again.

b. Recite tasbeeh of sajdah سُبْحَانَ رَبِّيَ الْاَعْلَى at least three times again.

The first rak'ah is now complete.

48

Say Allahu Akbar as you stand up for the qiyaam to begin the second rak'ah.
Now repeat the following:

a. recite Tasmiyah, Surah Faatihah, Tasmiyah again and a surah (at least three verses).

b. Ruku

c. Qawmah

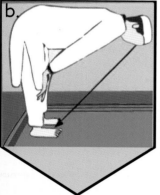

d. First sajdah

e. Jalsah

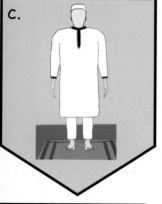

f. Second sajdah

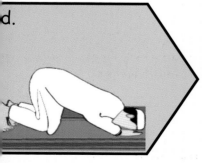

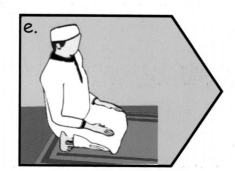

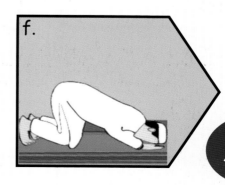

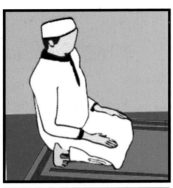

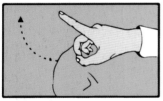

a. Whilst saying Allahu Akbar, sit up in the same way as you did for jalsah.

b. Now recite tashahhud.

- Upon reaching the words,

اَشْهَدُ اَنْ لَّاۤ اِلٰهَ

form a circle with the right thumb and the right middle finger.

- Raise the index finger of the right hand.

- Then lower the index finger upon reaching

اِلَّا اللّٰهُ

f. Recite Durood Ibrahim.

g. Recite the duaa after Durood Ibrahim.

12   Salaam (Final greeting to end the prayer)

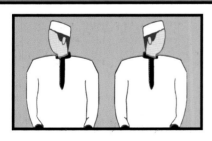

a. End the salaah by turning the head fully to the right and looking at the shoulder whilst reciting:

اَلسَّلَامُ عَلَيْكُمْ وَرَحْمَةُ اللّٰه

b. Do the same whilst turning the head to the left.

Two rak'aat salaah is now complete.

Girls' Salaah

How to learn to perform two rak'aats salaah using this book:

- Your teacher will show you how to perform each position of salaah correctly.

- Practice each position until it is perfect. After you have mastered all of the positions complete the activity on page 61.

- The recitation of Qur'aan and dua in salaah should be carried out softly. Whilst learning, recite loudly.

- All the Arabic duaas in salaah are on pages 58, 59 and 60.

1 Niyyah (Intention)

a. Stand upright facing the Qiblah, with the hands by the side and make the niyyah. For example: "I am performing two rak'aats fardh of Fajr salaah."

b. Focus the eyes towards the place of sajdah (prostration).

2 Takbeer Tahreemah (The first Allahu Akbar)

a. Raise the hands up to the shoulders preferably under the head scarf with both palms facing the Qiblah.

b. Keep the fingers together.

c. Then whilst saying Allahu Akbar fold both the hands as shown below in step three.

3 Qiyaam (Standing) - Folding the hands

a. Now place the right palm over the back of the left hand.

b. Keep the fingers together and elbows tucked in.

c. Place the hands on the middle of the chest, preferably under the headscarf.

4   Qiyaam (Standing) - Qir'aat (Recitation)

Now recite the following in order

a. Thanaa

b. Ta'awwudh

c. Tasmiyah

d. Surah Faatihah. Say Aameen softly at the end.

e. Tasmiyah

f. A surah (at least three verses)

5   Ruku (Bowing)

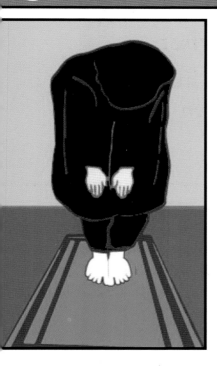

a. Whilst saying Allahu Akbar go into ruku (bowing).

b. In ruku only bend over enough so that the hands reach the knees.

c. The hands should be placed on the knees with the fingers together.

d. The arms should be touching the ribs and the elbows tucked in.

e. The ankles should be touching each other.

f. Recite the tasbeeh of ruku, سُبْحَانَ رَبِّيَ الْعَظِيْمِ at least three times.

g. Focus the eyes towards the feet.

6 Qawmah (Standing after ruku)

a. Recite tasmee' سَمِعَ اللّٰهُ لِمَنْ حَمِدَهُ whilst standing up from ruku, with the hands at the side.

b. Stand up straight and say the tahmeed رَبَّنَا وَلَكَ الْحَمْدُ.

c. Focus the eyes towards the place of sajdah (prostration).

d. Stay in this position until the whole body is relaxed.

7 First Sajdah (Prostration)

a. Now go into sajdah whilst saying Allahu Akbar.

b. Start bowing whilst going down.

c. Keep the elbows tucked in and the stomach close to the thighs.

d. Place your knees on the ground, and sit on the left bottom.

e. Place the feet out to the right with the toes facing towards the Qiblah. Ensure the feet are not upright.

f. Then place the hands on the ground followed by the nose and then finally the forehead.

g. Keep the elbows tucked in and the stomach touching the thighs.

h. Recite the tasbeeh of sajdah سُبْحَانَ رَبِّيَ الْأَعْلٰى at least three times.

8   Jalsah (Sitting)

a. Whilst saying Allahu Akbar sit up and place the hands on the thighs.

b. Keep the fingers together.

c. The feet should be sticking out towards the right whilst sitting.

d. The toes should be pointing towards the Qiblah.

e. Focus the eyes towards the lap.

9   Second Sajdah

a. Whilst saying Allahu Akbar go into sajdah again.

b. Recite tasbeeh of sajdah سُبْحَانَ رَبِّيَ الْأَعْلَى at least three times again.

The first rak'ah is now complete.

55

Say Allahu Akbar as you stand up for the qiyaam to begin the second rak'ah.
Now repeat the following:

a. recite Tasmiyah, Surah Faatihah, Tasmiyah again and a surah (at least three verses).

b. Ruku

c. Qawmah

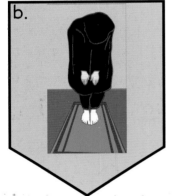

d. First sajdah

e. Jalsah

f. Second sajdah

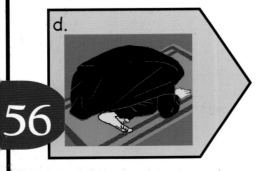
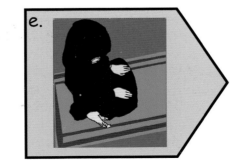
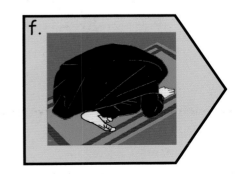

11 Qa'dah Aakhirah (Final Sitting)

a. Whilst saying Allahu Akbar, sit up in the same way as you did for jalsah.

b. Now recite tashahhud.
- Upon reaching the words,

  form a circle with the right thumb and the right middle finger.

- Raise the index finger of the right hand.
- Then lower the index finger upon reaching

f. Recite Durood Ibrahim.

g. Recite the duaa after Durood Ibrahim.

12 Salaam (Final greeting to end the prayer)

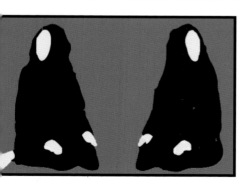

a. End the salaah by turning the head fully to the right and looking at the shoulder whilst reciting

b. Do the same whilst turning the head to the left.

Two rak'aat salaah is now complete.

Duaas in Salaah

Takbeer

اَللّٰهُ اَكْبَرُ

Allah is the Greatest

Thanaa

سُبْحَانَكَ اللّٰهُمَّ وَبِحَمْدِكَ وَتَبَارَكَ اسْمُكَ وَتَعَالٰى جَدُّكَ وَلَا اِلٰهَ غَيْرُكَ ○

*Glory be to You O Allah, praise be to You, and blessed
is Your name, very lofty is Your greatness, and there is no one worthy of worship
besides You.*

Ta'awwudh

اَعُوْذُ بِاللّٰهِ مِنَ الشَّيْطَانِ الرَّجِيْمِ ○

I seek protection in Allah from Shaytaan, the rejected.

Tasmiyah

بِسْمِ اللّٰهِ الرَّحْمٰنِ الرَّحِيْمِ ○

In the name of Allah, the Most Beneficent, the Most Merciful .

Surah Faatihah

All praise is due to Allah, the Lord of the Worlds.	اَلْحَمْدُ لِلّٰهِ رَبِّ الْعَالَمِيْنَ ○
The most Kind, the most Merciful	الرَّحْمٰنِ الرَّحِيْمِ ○
Master of the Day of Judgment.	مٰلِكِ يَوْمِ الدِّيْنِ ○
You alone do we worship, and You alone do we ask for help.	اِيَّاكَ نَعْبُدُ وَاِيَّاكَ نَسْتَعِيْنُ ○
Guide us to the straight path.	اِهْدِنَا الصِّرَاطَ الْمُسْتَقِيْمَ ○
The path of those whom you have favoured.	صِرَاطَ الَّذِيْنَ اَنْعَمْتَ عَلَيْهِمْ ۙ
Not of those who have earned your anger, nor those who have gone astray.	غَيْرِ الْمَغْضُوْبِ عَلَيْهِمْ وَلَا الضَّآلِّيْنَ ○

Duaas in Salaah

Tasbeeh in Ruku

سُبْحَانَ رَبِّيَ الْعَظِيمِ

Glory be to my Lord, the Great

Tasmee'

سَمِعَ اللّٰهُ لِمَنْ حَمِدَهُ

Allah hears the one who praises Him.

Tahmeed

رَبَّنَا وَلَكَ الْحَمْدُ

Our Lord, to You belongs all praise.

Tasbeeh in Sajdah

سُبْحَانَ رَبِّيَ الْاَعْلٰى

Glory be to my Lord, the Most High

Tashahhud

اَلتَّحِيَّاتُ لِلّٰهِ وَالصَّلَوٰتُ وَالطَّيِّبَاتُ ۝

اَلسَّلَامُ عَلَيْكَ اَيُّهَا النَّبِيُّ وَرَحْمَةُ اللّٰهِ وَبَرَكَاتُهُ ۝

اَلسَّلَامُ عَلَيْنَا وَعَلٰى عِبَادِ اللّٰهِ الصَّالِحِينَ ۝

اَشْهَدُ اَنْ لَّا اِلٰهَ اِلَّا اللّٰهُ ۝ وَاَشْهَدُ اَنَّ مُحَمَّدًا عَبْدُهُ وَرَسُوْلُهُ ۝

All devotions offered through words, bodily actions and wealth are due to Allah.

Peace be upon you, O Prophet and the mercy of Allah and His blessings.

Peace be upon us and on the pious (righteous) servants of Allah.

I bear witness that there is no one worthy of worship besides Allah, and I bear witness that Muhammad is His servant and messenger.

Duaas in Salaah

Durood Ibrahim

اَللّٰهُمَّ صَلِّ عَلٰى مُحَمَّدٍ ۞ وَّ عَلٰى اٰلِ مُحَمَّدٍ ۞ كَمَا صَلَّيْتَ عَلٰى اِبْرٰهِيْمَ ۞ وَ عَلٰى اٰلِ اِبْرٰهِيْمَ ۞ اِنَّكَ حَمِيْدٌ مَّجِيْدٌ ۞

اَللّٰهُمَّ بَارِكْ عَلٰى مُحَمَّدٍ ۞ وَّ عَلٰى اٰلِ مُحَمَّدٍ ۞ كَمَا بَارَكْتَ عَلٰى اِبْرٰهِيْمَ ۞ وَ عَلٰى اٰلِ اِبْرٰهِيْمَ ۞ اِنَّكَ حَمِيْدٌ مَّجِيْدٌ ۞

O Allah shower Your mercy on Muhammad and his family (followers) as You showered Your mercy on Ibrahim and his family (followers).

Surely You are Praiseworthy and Most High.

O Allah bless Muhammad and his family (followers) as You have blessed Ibrahim and his family (followers).

Surely You are Praiseworthy and Most High.

Dua after Durood Shareef

اَللّٰهُمَّ اِنِّيْ ظَلَمْتُ نَفْسِيْ ظُلْمًا كَثِيْرًا ۞ وَّاِنَّهٗ لَا يَغْفِرُ الذُّنُوْبَ اِلَّا اَنْتَ ۞ فَاغْفِرْ لِيْ مَغْفِرَةً مِّنْ عِنْدِكَ وَارْحَمْنِيْ ۞ اِنَّكَ اَنْتَ الْغَفُوْرُ الرَّحِيْمُ ۞

O Allah I have wronged myself greatly and nobody forgives sins except You.

Grant me forgiveness and have mercy on me.

Surely, You are The Forgiver and The Merciful.

Salaam

اَلسَّلَامُ عَلَيْكُمْ وَرَحْمَةُ اللّٰه

May Allah's peace and blessings be upon you.

Activity

Once you feel you have mastered a position fill in the table below with signatures from your partner, parent and teacher.

Position	1st My partner has seen me do it correctly	2nd My parent has seen me do it correctly	3rd My teacher has seen me do it correctly
Takbeer Tahreemah			
Qiyaam			
Ruku			
Qawmah			
Sajdah			
Jalsah			
Qa'dah Aakhirah			
Salaam			
Full two rakaats			

Now go back to the 'What am I learning?' section for this lesson and tick if you have met the objectives.

NOTES